Alpha Book Publisher
www.alphapublisher.com

Ordering Information:
Quantity sales. Special discounts are available on quantity purchases by corporations, associations, and others. For orders by U.S. trade bookstores and wholesalers, contact the Publisher at:
www.alphapublisher.com/contact-us to learn more.

Printed in the United States of America.

Kingsley and Bob go to the Park

written by:
Dustin-Lee Tucker

Hi, I'm Kingsley. This is Bob my best friend. Today, mom is bringing Bob and me to the park. There are so many fun things to do at the park.

Kingsley said, "They have slides, swings, merry-go-round, seesaw, and so many fun things to do and see."

Have fun

Kingsley said, "I love the swings. When I swing on the swings, I feel like I'm flying like a bird in the sky."

"go higher"

"Swing higher, Kingsley!" Bob says. " Kingsley responds, "I'm scared the swings go really high, like to the sky!" Bob responds, "The swing goes high because the sky is the limit, and you can be free like a bird." Kingsley begins to swing higher toward the sky.

yeah

Bob invited Kingsley to ride the seesaw. "I love the seesaw; I feel like I can hop as high as skyscrapers," Kingsley said.

"Hop higher," Bob says to Kingsley. "I'm scared, Bob, to hop that high." Bob responds, "You can hop over your fears and be as strong as a skyscraper." Kingsley begins to hop high toward the treetops.

Yay

"Look, Bob!" Kingsley exclaimed as he rode the merry-go-round. Let's spin as fast as we can. Bob loves the merry-go-round because it spins from a different point of view.

"Spin faster," Kingsley says to Bob. "I'm scared to spin that fast," Bob responds. Kingsley tells Bob, "You can spin any situation into a positive one with a positive point of view." Bob starts spinning fast, and everything becomes a wheel of colors.

"We have to go down the slide, come on let's go," Kingsley says to Bob. Bob enjoys the slide because it allows him to be free.

"Slide faster," Kingsley says to Bob. Bob replies, "I'm scared to slide faster." Kingsley responds, "You have the freedom to slide into the future you desire." Bob begins to slide faster until he can't slide anymore.

"Time to go home, little ones," Mom yells. Did you have a lot of fun at the park today? "YES!" said Kingsley and Bob.

Bob and Kingsley returned home. They talked about how much fun they had at the park. "We can conquer anything we set our minds to," Kingsley says to Bob. Bob agreed.

"We are brave!"

"We are strong!"

"We Can Do Anything!"

"Hey Kingsley, I can't wait for our next adventure!"

Made in United States
North Haven, CT
30 January 2023